# FINGERPRINT FUN
# WILD ANIMALS

## KATE DAUBNEY

ARCTURUS

ARCTURUS

This edition published in 2017 by Arcturus Publishing Limited
26/27 Bickels Yard, 151–153 Bermondsey Street,
London SE1 3HA, UK

Illustrated by Kate Daubney
Written and edited by Susannah Bailey
Designed by Square and Circus

ISBN: 978-1-78428-802-0
CH005658NT
Supplier 29 Date 0717 Print run 6138

Printed in China

# FINGERPRINTING IS FUN!

In this book you'll learn how to paint your very own fingerprint animals. To do this, you'll need to use different parts of your fingers.

normal fingerprint

finger smudge

fingertip

thumb print

hand print

## OUR TOP TIPS:

**1.** Make sure you have a wet cloth or tissues nearby to change the paint on your fingers.

**2.** Only add a tiny amount of water to your paints, or they'll become too runny.

**3.** Experiment with how much paint you put on your finger. The smaller the amount of paint, the quicker the print will dry!

**4.** Leave your prints to dry before you add the black linework.

**5.** You may find it easier to make some prints by turning the page around or upside down.

# JUNGLE FLOCK

Here's how to paint a perching parrot.

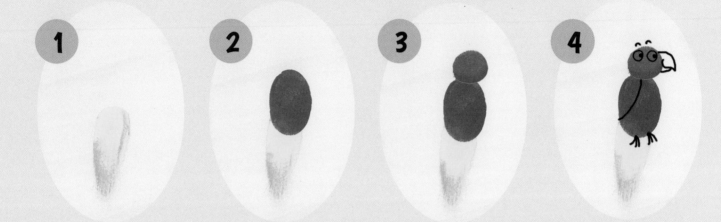

And here's a flying parrot! Can you make one, too?

Fill this tree with a flock of jungle parrots!

# FRIENDLY FOX

Follow the steps to make this cheerful creature.

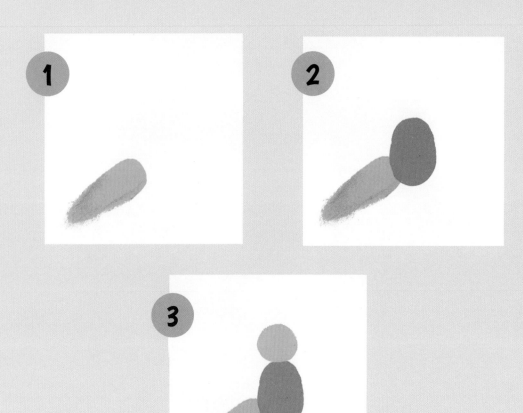

# BUNNY BURROW

Add bright, fluffy fingerprint tails to these rabbits.

# STRIPY ZEBRA

Can you create a zebra using only your handprint?

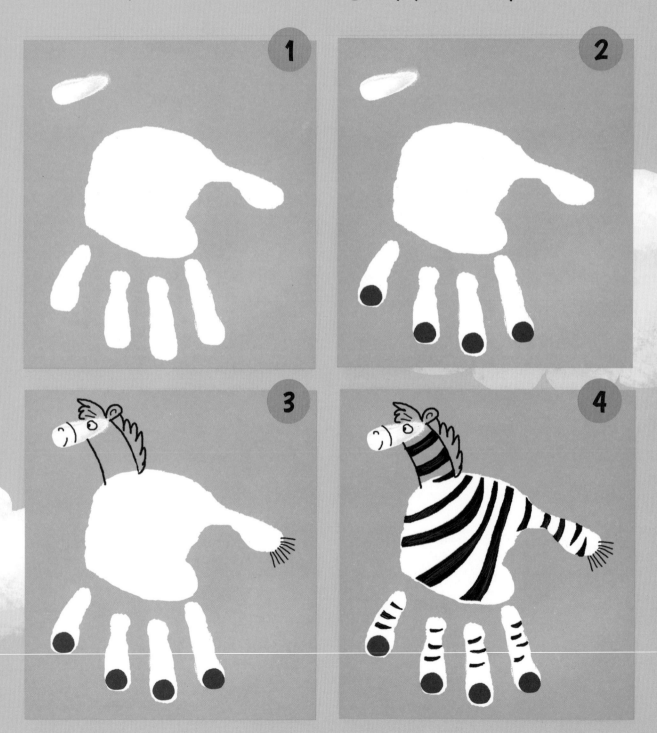

Add your own zebra to
this grazing scene.

# LITTLE LIZARD

Here's how to make a scampering lizard.

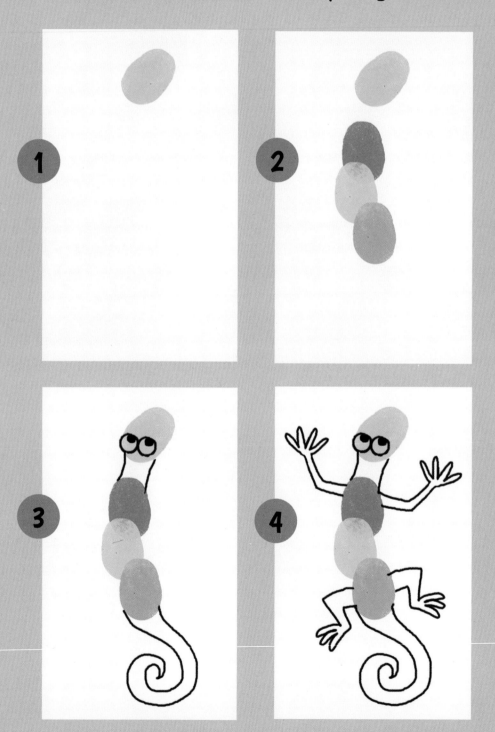

# SLOW AND STEADY

Follow the steps to make a really cute tortoise.

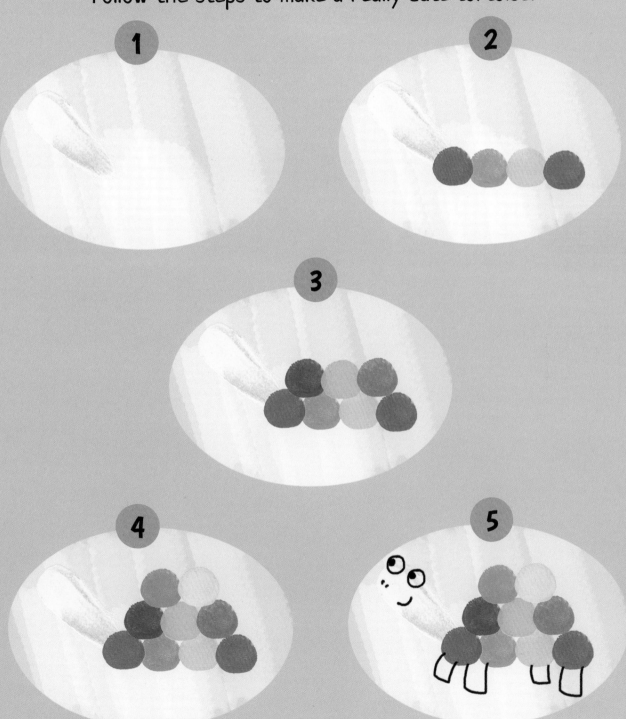

# HAPPY CATERPILLAR

Can you create a crawling caterpillar?

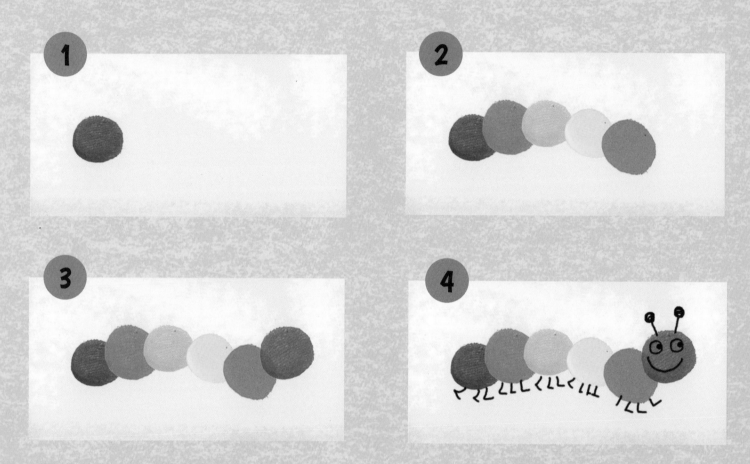

Add some extra legs to turn it into a millipede!

Fill the tree branches with crunching caterpillars and millipedes.

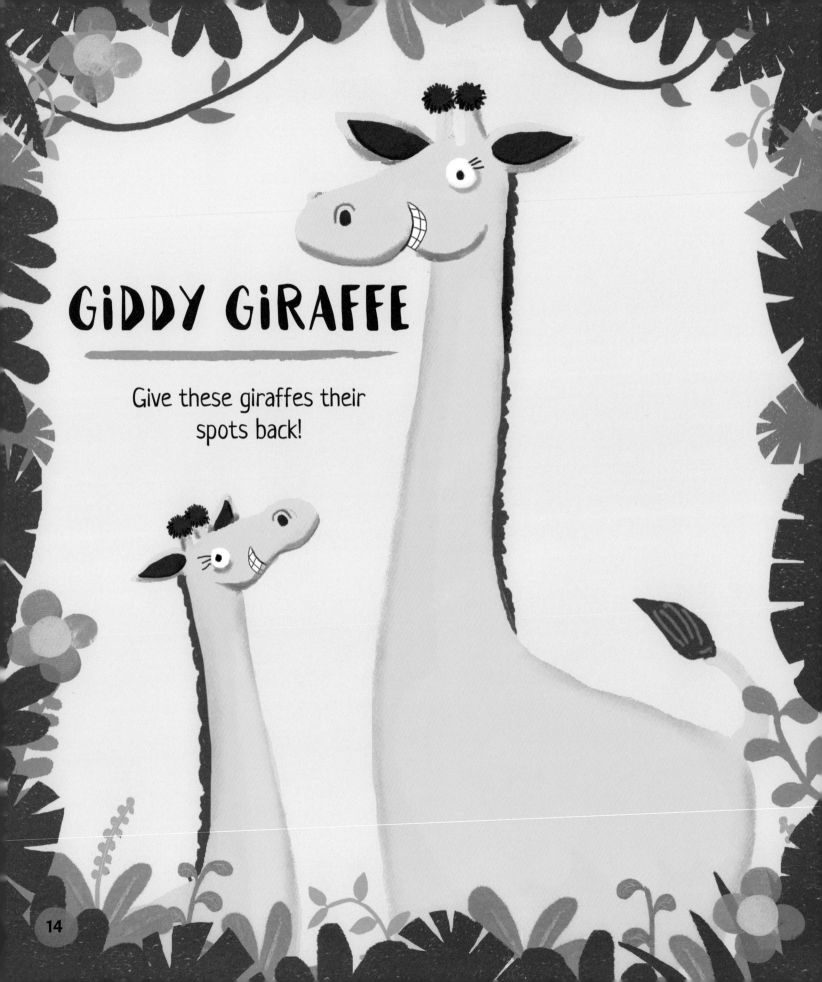

# GIDDY GIRAFFE

Give these giraffes their
spots back!

# YAWNING HIPPO

Paint fingerprint teeth in
this hippo's mouth.

# POND LIFE

Follow the steps to make a swimming tadpole.

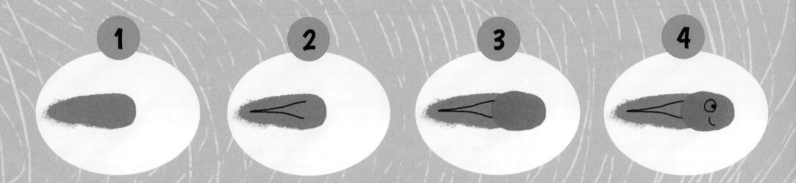

Tadpoles turn into frogs! Can you make the frog below?

Add some frogs sitting on
the lily pads.

# BRiGHT BEETLE

Creating a cute creepy-crawly is easy!

# WATCH OUT!

Print some patterns on this curious iguana.

# POSING PEACOCK

Use your handprint to make a bird with eye-catching feathers.

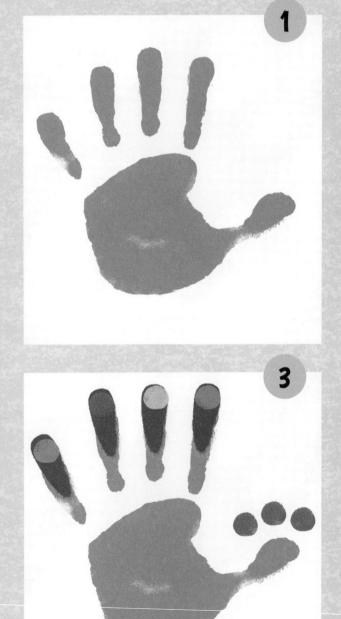

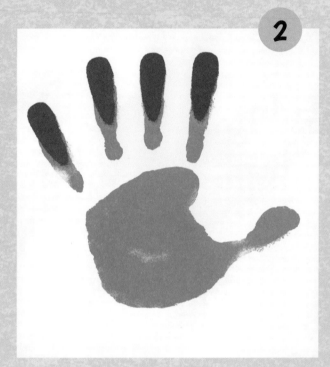

Add a peacock to this garden scene.

# TEENY MOUSE

Follow these steps to make a mouse.

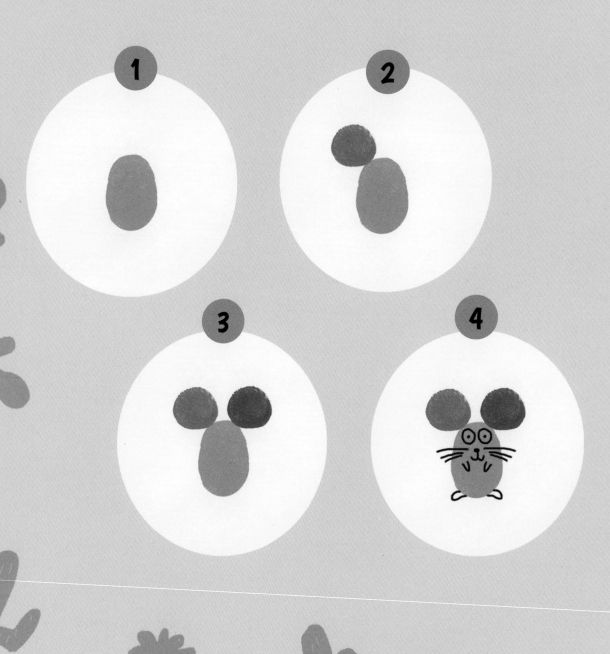

# FUNNY BUNNY

Can you create a cute little rabbit?

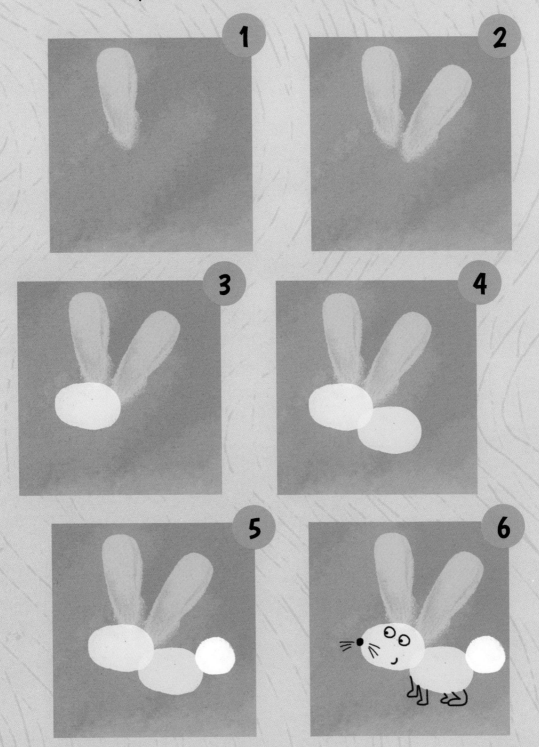

# BUZZING BEE

Here's how to make a smiling bee.

Now, fill the hives with busy bees!

# BEWARE, BEARS!

Add some yummy fruit for the bears to pick.

# CHARMING DEER

Print some white markings on these forest friends.

# PLAYFUL MONKEY

Here's how to make a swinging monkey.

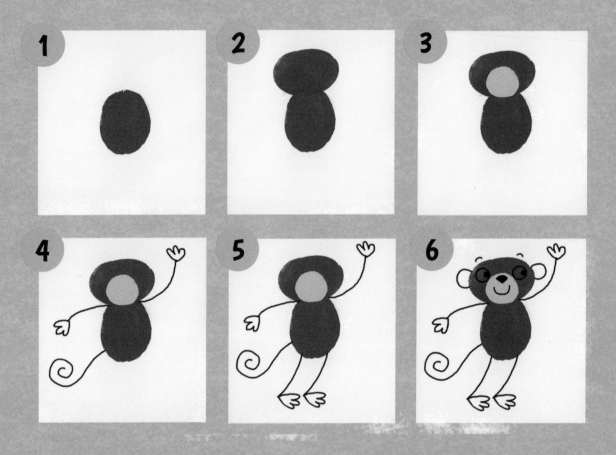

Now, make a baby monkey!

Monkeys love bananas! Fill the tree with hungry creatures.

# HiSSSSSS!

Add spots to this sneaky snake.

# TOUGH RHINO

Follow the steps to create this horned animal.

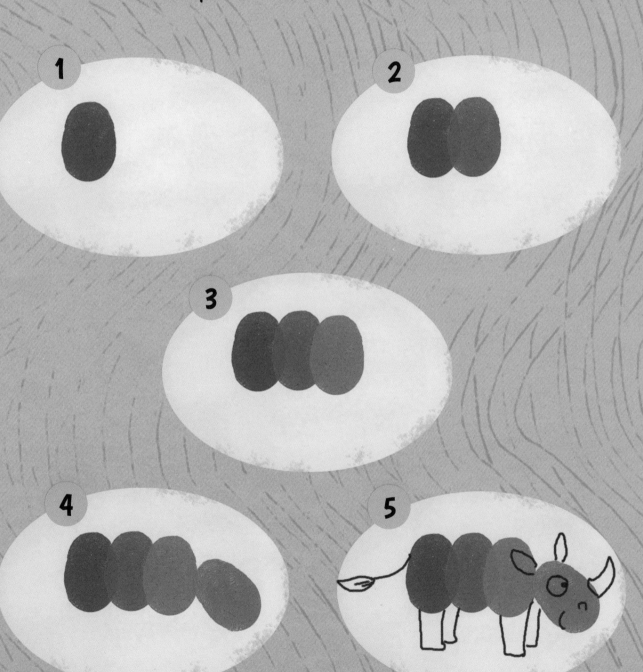

# FLYING FRIENDS

Will you make a beautiful butterfly ...

... or a magnificent moth?

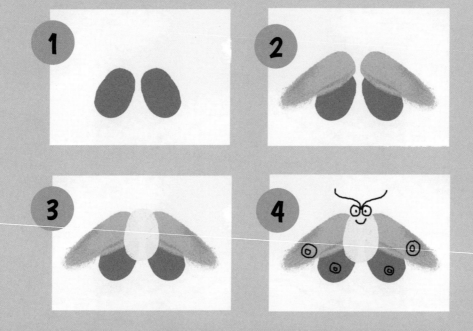

Add some fluttering butterflies
to the flowers!

# DAZZLING DRAGONFLY

Follow the steps to make this winged creature.

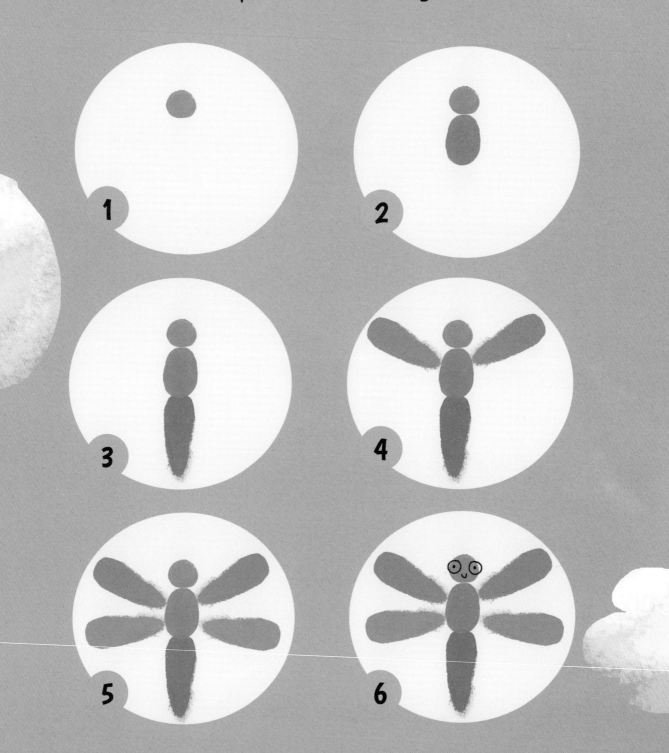

# SNAPPING CROC

Here's how to paint a hungry crocodile.

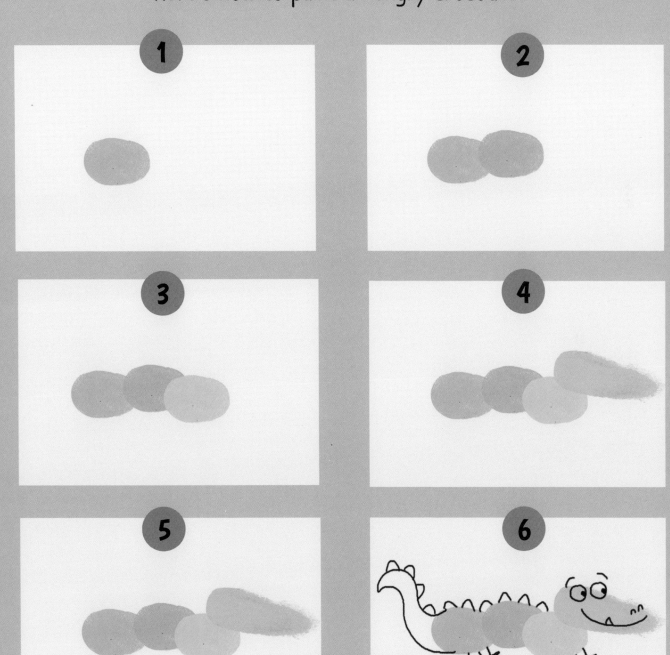

# SPOTTED LEOPARD

Add spots to your handprint to make this big cat.

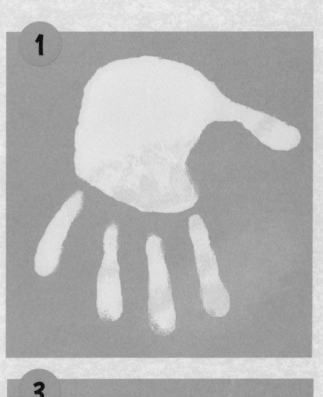

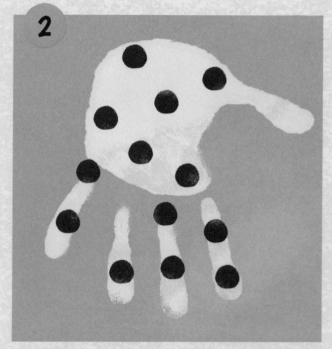

Paint a leopard hunting its prey.

# BUSY BUGS

Add some fingerprint spots to brighten up these bugs.

Print some patterns on
these snails' shells.

# CHIPMUNK CHARM

Follow the steps to make an adorable chipmunk.

# FRiENDLY FiSH

Decorate the fish, and add fingerprint bubbles coming from their mouths.

# MR. MEERKAT

Here's how to make a smiling meerkat.

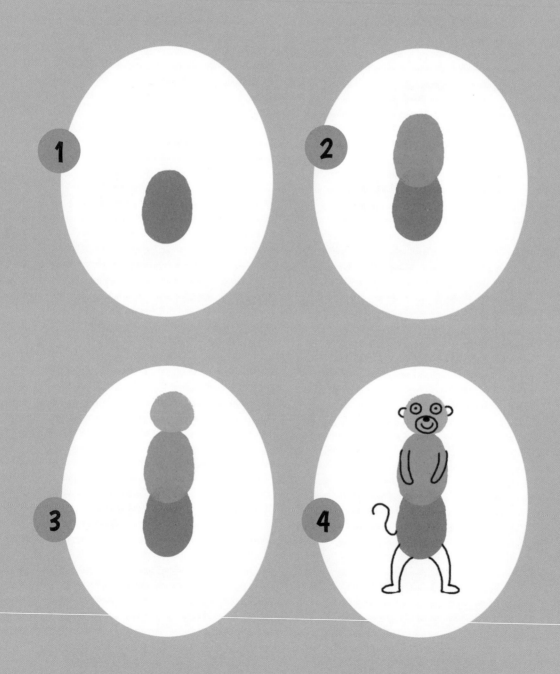

# LOOK UP!

Add some spots to this
wild lynx.

# FANTASTIC FLAMINGO

Follow the steps to make this eye-catching bird.

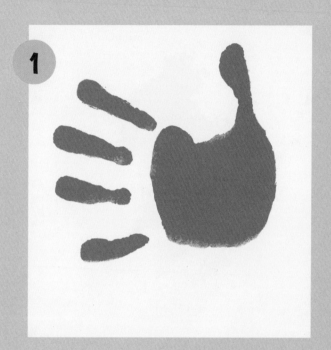

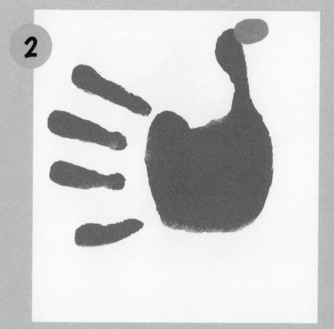

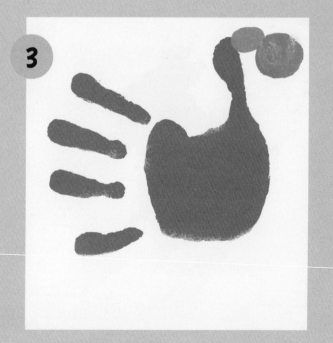

Print a pair of flamingos walking in the water.

# SWIMMING SEA HORSE

Here's how to paint this water creature.

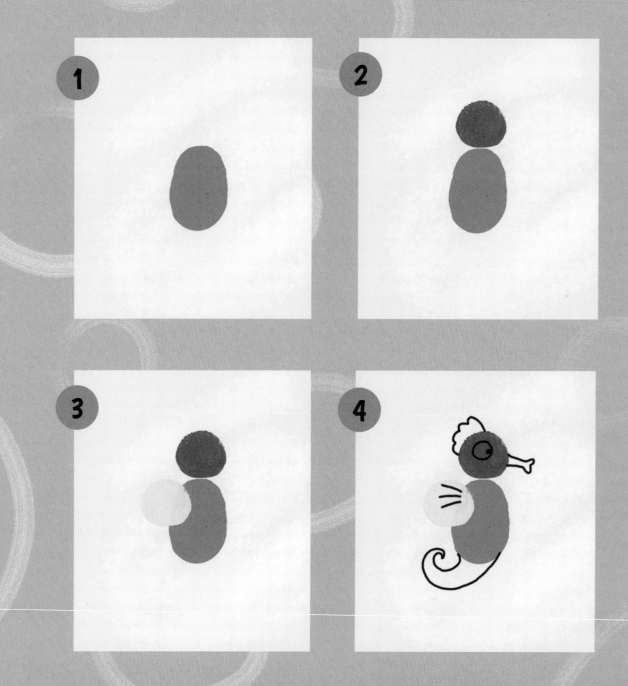

# COOL RACCOON

Follow the steps to create a raccoon.

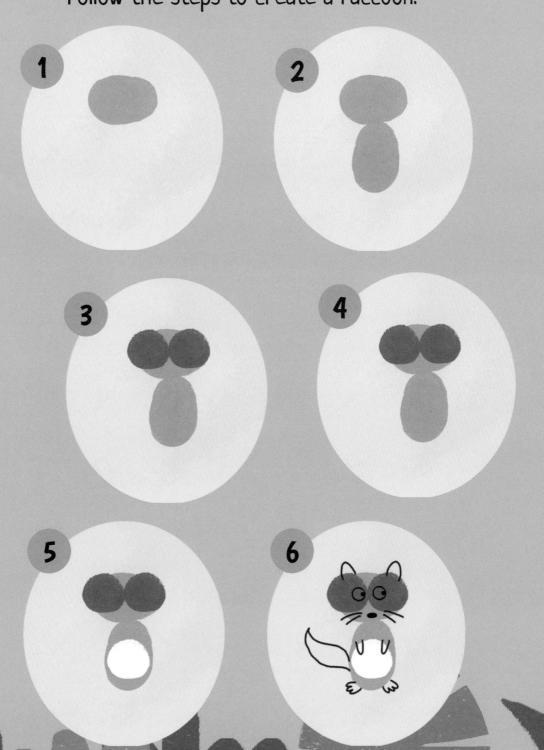

# SMILING SNAIL

Can you follow the steps to make this happy creature?

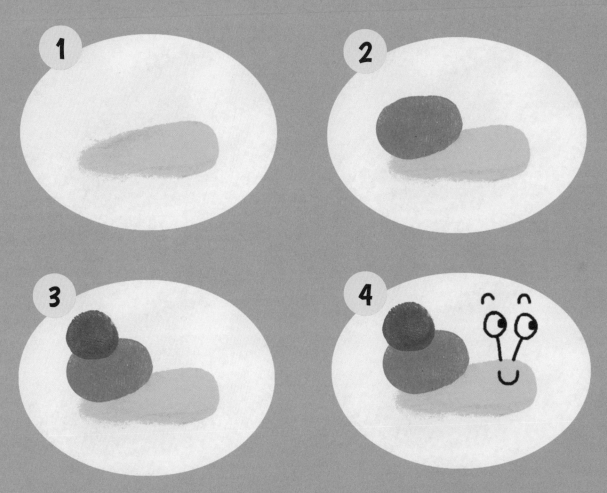

Or use different paints for a whole new look!

Cover the toadstools with fingerprint snails.

# BiG BUFFALO

Here's how to paint a giant buffalo.

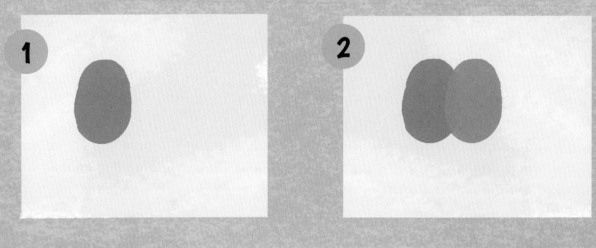

# THE MANE EVENT

Give this fingerprint lion an eye-catching mane.

# WiSE OWL

Follow the steps to make an adorable owl.

Now, fill this owl's nest with eggs
of different sizes.

# TROPICAL TOUCAN

Follow the steps to make a big-billed bird.

# GALLOPING GAZELLE

Can you make this forest creature?

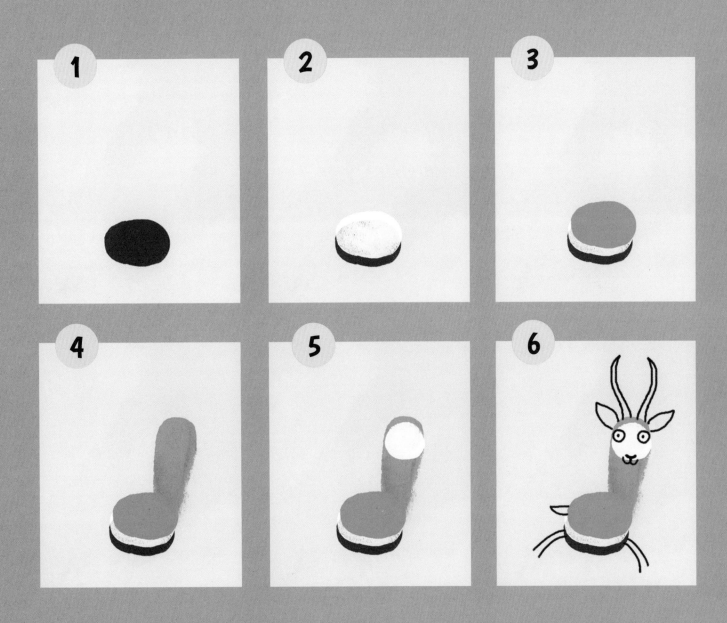

# CUTE PANDA

Try painting a panda face.

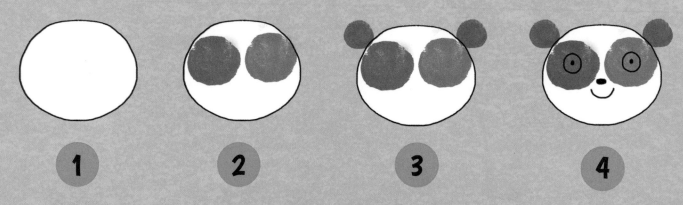

1     2     3     4

Or try painting a whole panda body!

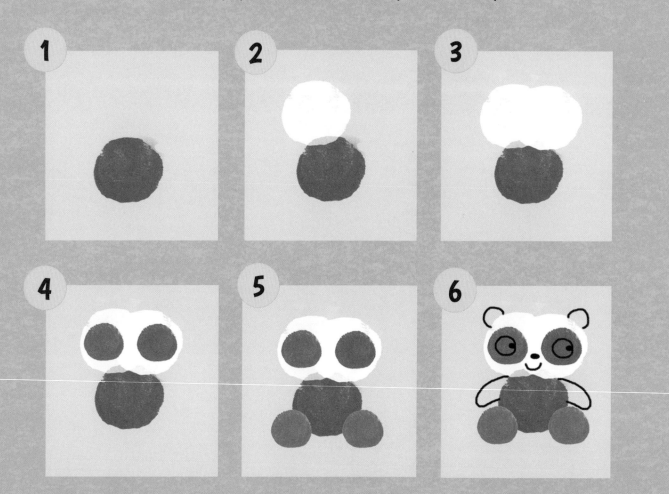

1     2     3

4     5     6

Add some pandas climbing on the bamboo.

# WOODLAND SQUIRREL

Here's how to make a cute squirrel.

# PRICKLY HEDGEHOG

Follow the steps to make this pointy animal.

# AWESOME OSTRICH

Use your whole hand to create this huge bird.

1

2

3

4

Add another ostrich to this grassy scene.

# SLITHERING SNAKE

Here's how to make this coiled reptile.

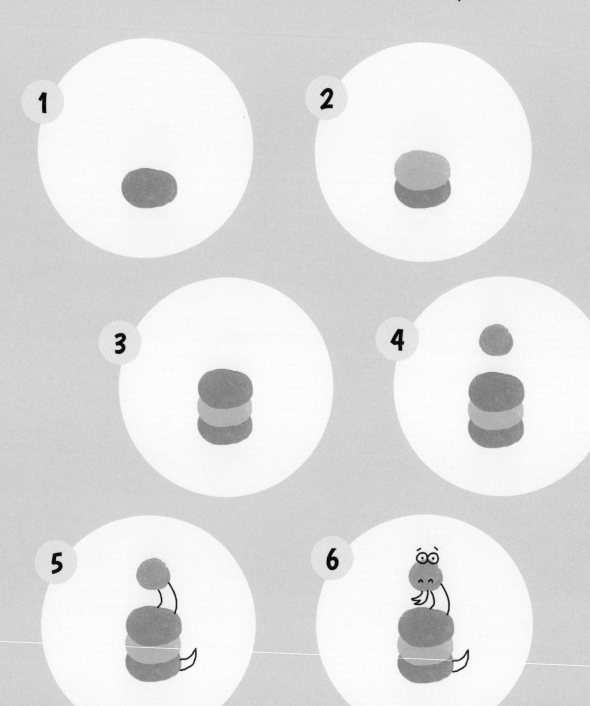

# HA, HA, HA!

Print spots on the laughing hyenas.

# SPINNING SPIDER

Follow the steps to create this eight-legged insect.

Add a spider to this web.

# OTTER-LY ADORABLE

Here's how to paint a playful otter.

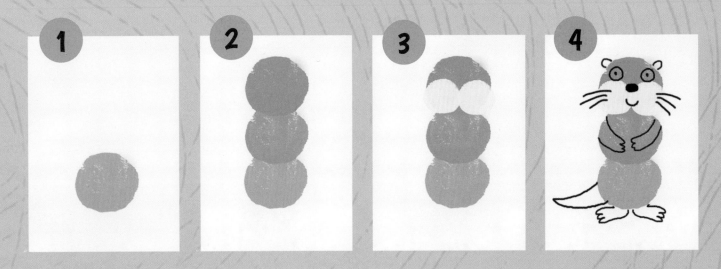

Zzzzz ... Now, make a sleepy otter.

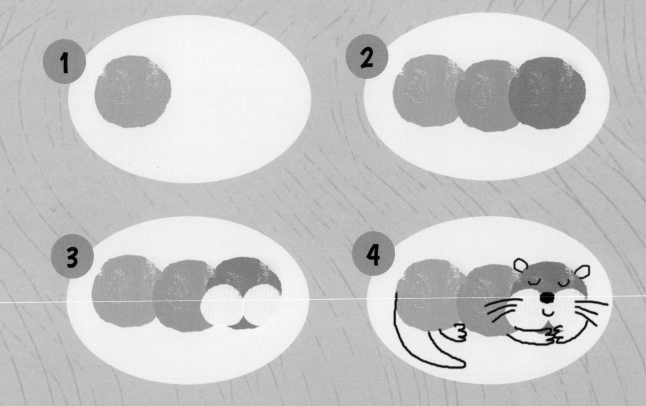

# GATHERING NUTS

Add more acorns for this hungry squirrel
to eat.

# PRANCING REINDEER

Use your whole hand to make this wintry animal.

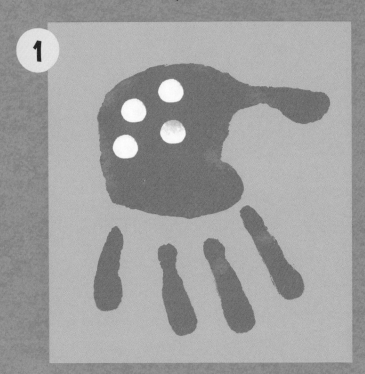

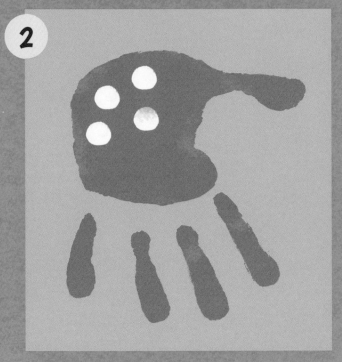

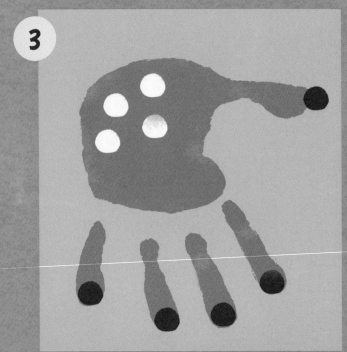

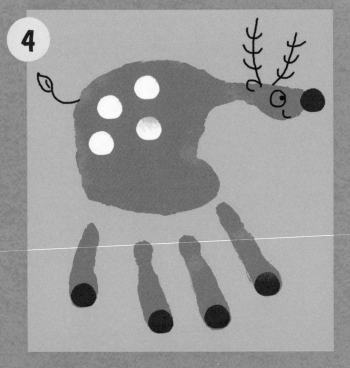

Complete this snowy scene with a reindeer.

# FURRY HUNTER

Here's how to paint a running wolf.

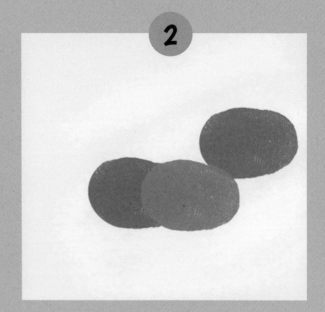

# BOLD BADGER

Follow the steps to make this clever creature.

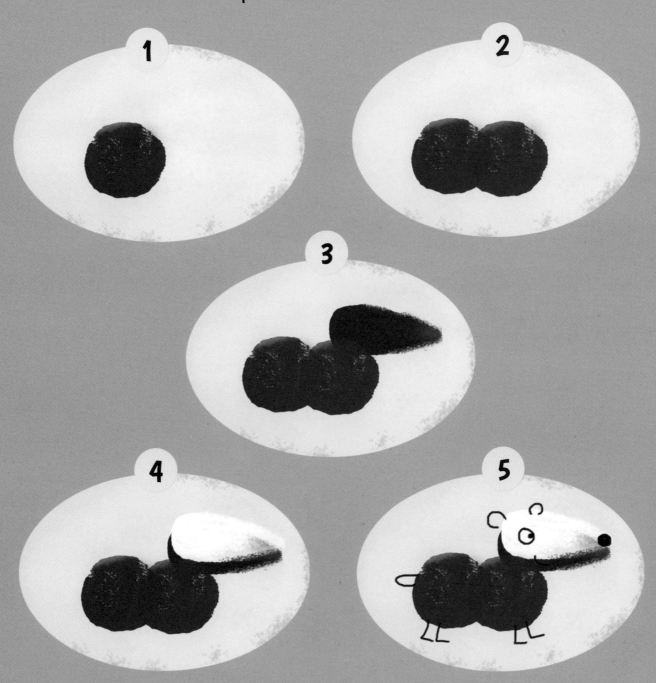

# BUSY BEAVER

Here's how to make a cute face.

Now, make a beaver's body!

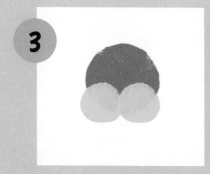

Add some more busy beavers to this dam.

# BOLD BABOON

Follow the steps to make an unusual animal.

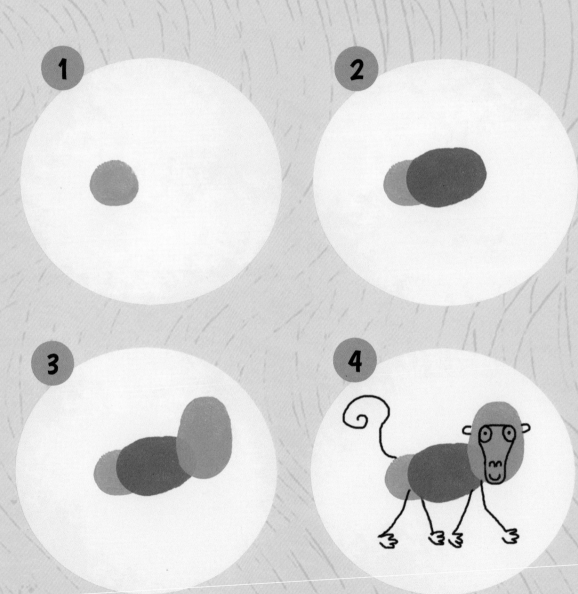

# HiDE-AND-SEEK

Add some spots to these chameleons, so that they blend in with the leaves.

# MIGHTY ELEPHANT

Use your handprint to make this exotic creature.

# BALD EAGLE

Can you follow the steps to paint this bird of prey?

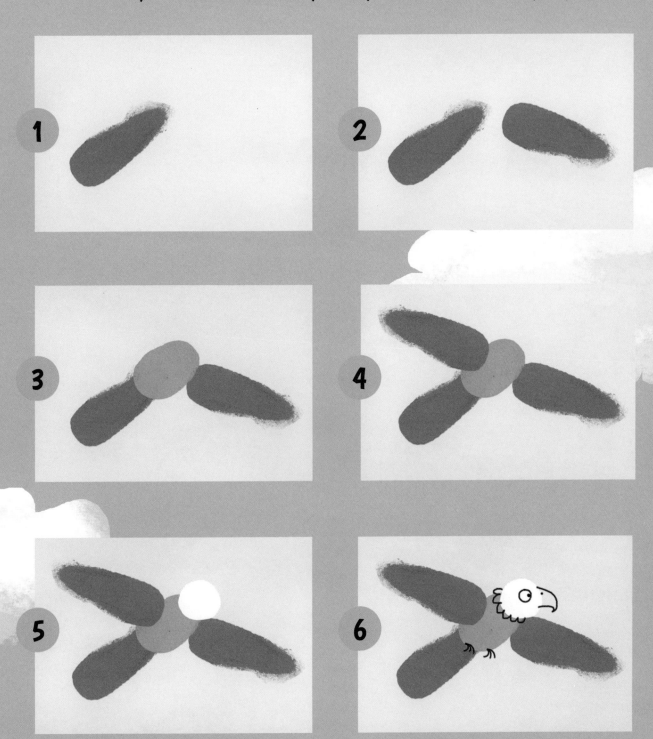

# AMAZING ANTS

Will you paint a garden ant?     Or will you make a fighting army ant?

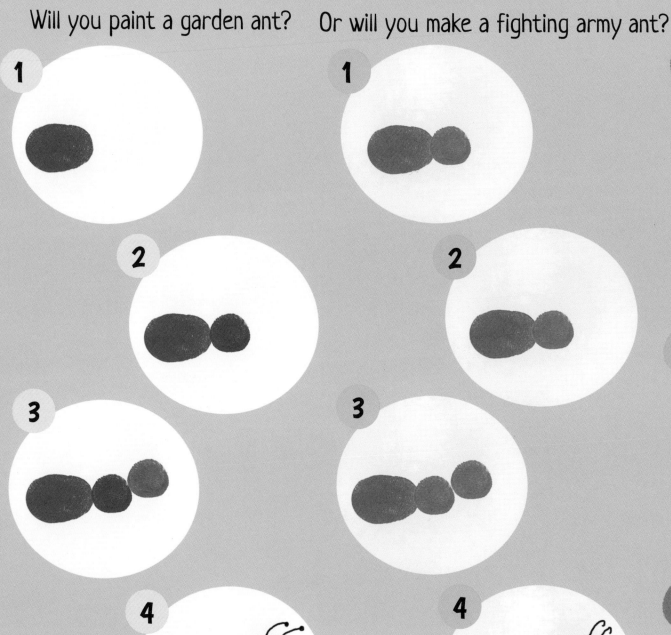

# BRIGHT BUTTERFLIES

Paint patterns
on these
beautiful butterflies.

# GRIZZLY BEAR

Follow the steps to make a bear on the prowl ...

... or paint a bear stopping to rest.

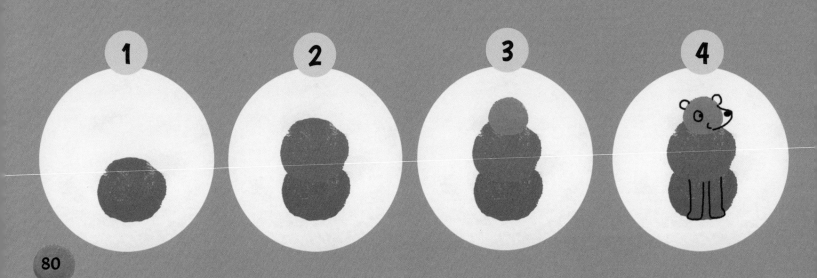

A bear made these paw prints.
Add the creature to the path!

# SAVAGE SHARK

Here's how to make a fierce hunter.

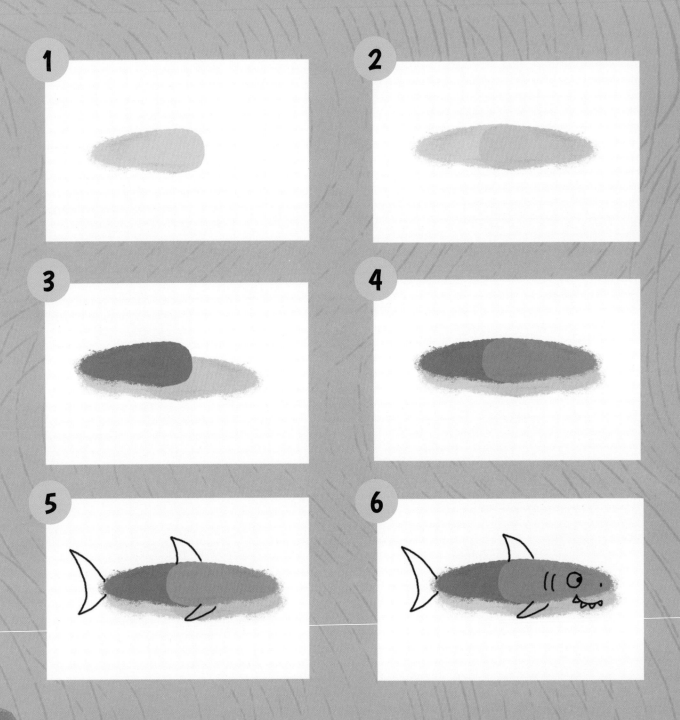

# JUMPING ANTELOPE

Can you paint this leaping animal?

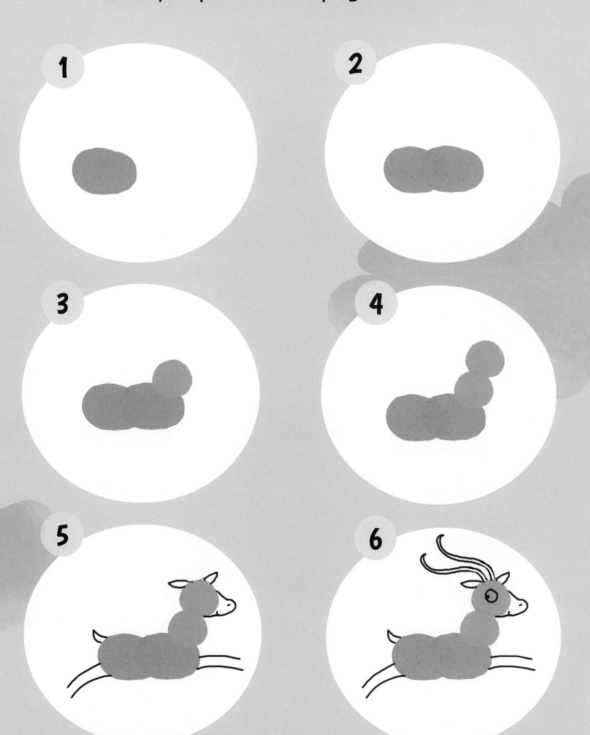

# MONKEYING AROUND

Make a monkey from your handprint with these steps.

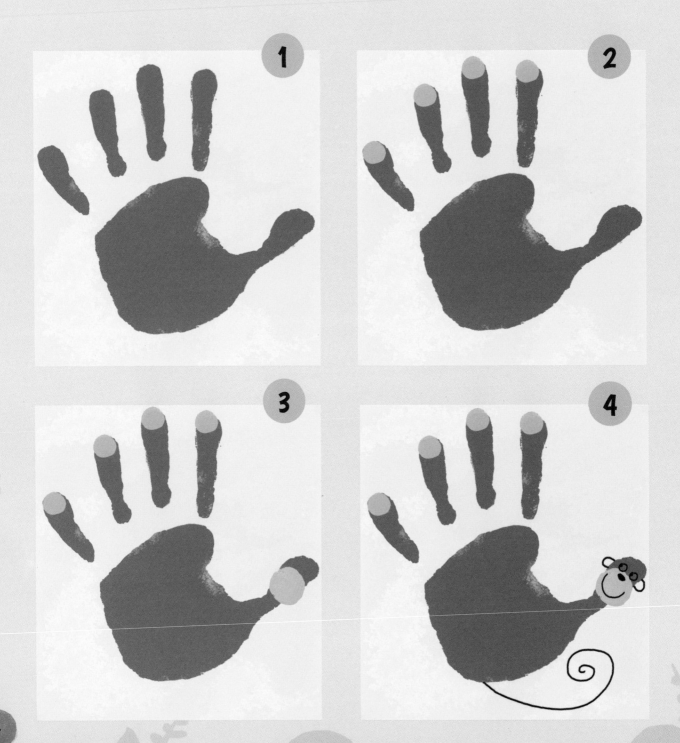

Add a handprint monkey
swinging from the tree.

# HUNGRY GORILLA

Add some fingerprint fruit for this gorilla to eat.

# WILD PONIES

Give these happy ponies manes and tails.

# JUNGLE TiGER

Roar! Follow the steps to paint this fierce animal.

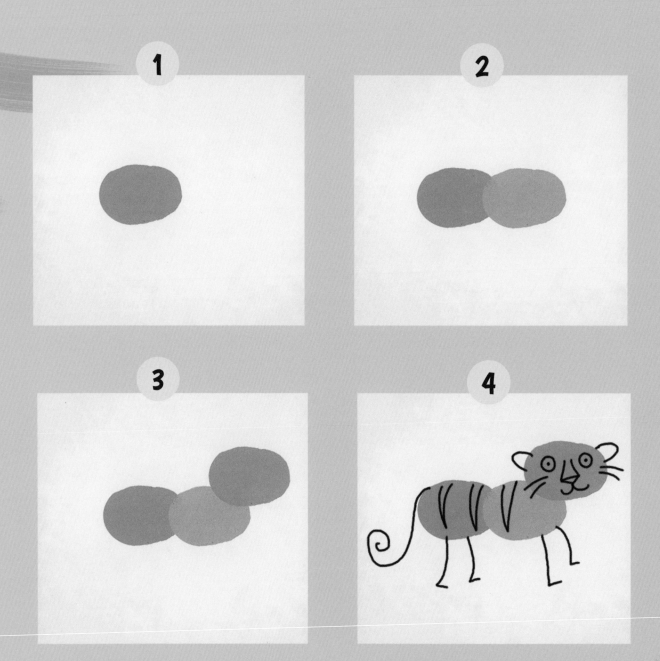

# STRIPY LEMUR

Here's how to paint a mischievous lemur.

# HAPPY HiPPO

Follow the steps to make a cheerful hippo.

**1**

**2**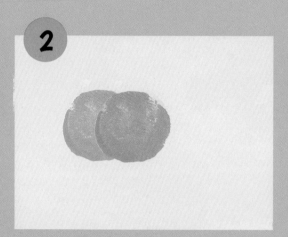

**3**

**4**

**5**

**6**

# COCKATOO CRESTS

Add some head feathers to these fancy birds.

# CHEERFUL CHEETAH

Use your whole hand to make a spotted cheetah.

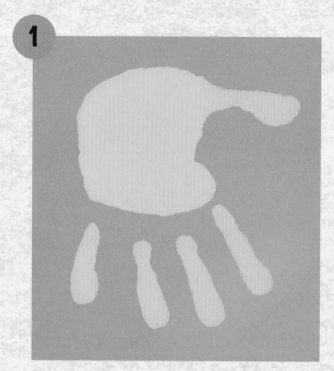

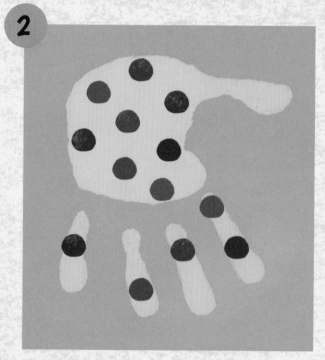

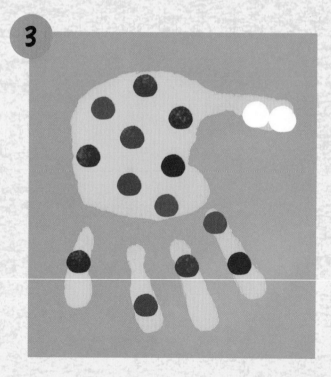

Add a mother cheetah guarding her cubs.

# MIDNIGHT BAT

Here's how to make a flying bat.

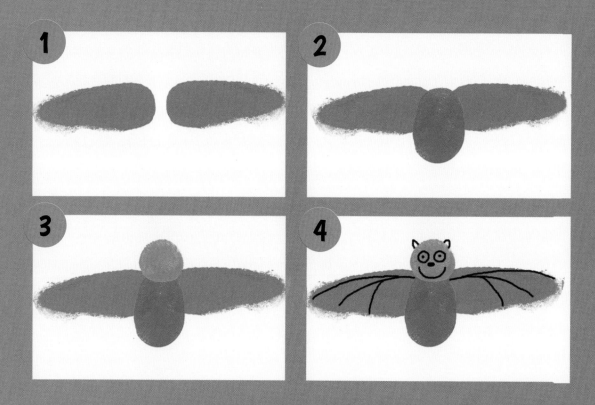

Now, make a hanging bat!

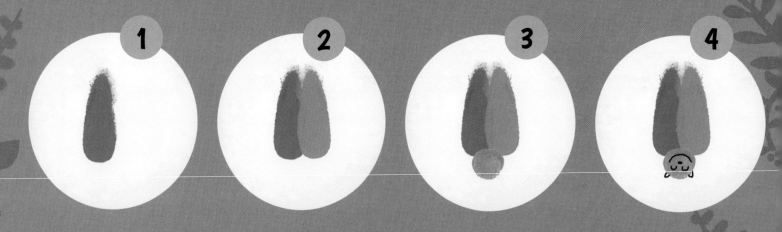

# ELEGANT HORSE

Can you paint a horse's head ...

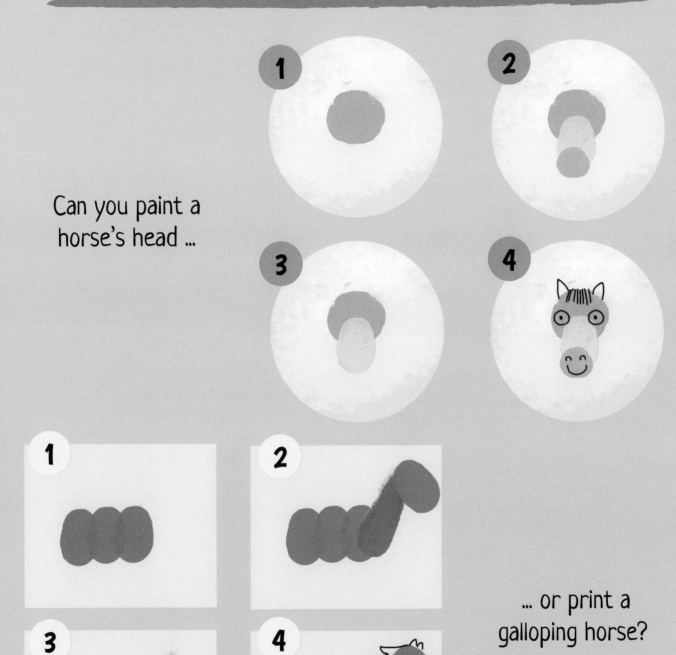

... or print a galloping horse?

# RED ROBIN

Finish the book by making a little red robin!

**1**

**2**

**3**

**4**